a b c

Aa Bb Cc Dd Ee
Ff Gg Hh Ii Jj Kk
Ll Mm Nn Oo Pp
Qq Rr Ss Tt Uu
Vv Ww Xx Yy Zz

This book belongs to

....

Peppa and George are learning their ABC.

Letter names
ABCDEFGHIJKLM

Letter sounds
abcdefghijklm

Point to each letter as you say it along with Peppa and George.

NOPQRSTUVWXYZ

nopqrstuvwxyz

What letter does your name start with?

A

Write your name here and draw a picture of yourself.

ANEG

A

a is for apple

Grandpa Pig grows apples in his garden. Hidden in the picture is a creature whose name starts with the sound **a**. Can you spot it?

Answer: ant.

b is for bicycle

Look at Peppa on her bicycle. Draw a picture of yourself on a bicycle here, so that you can ride with Peppa.

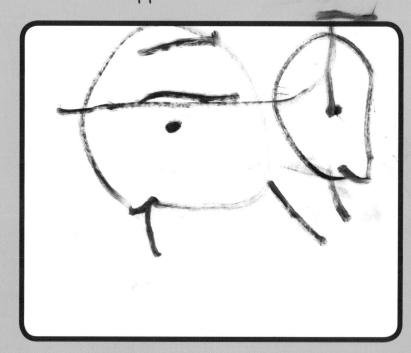

C is for car

Peppa and her family love to go for a ride in their car.
What else in this picture begins with the sound **C**?

Answer: cloud.

d is for dinosaur

George's favourite toy is Mr Dinosaur.
Draw a circle around all the dinosaurs you can see in the picture.

a b c d e f g h i j k l m n o p q r s t u v w x y z

e is for elephant

Emily Elephant is one of Peppa's friends. There is a funny elephant face in the picture. Draw a ring around it when you find it. Then trace the path of the letter **e** with your pencil.

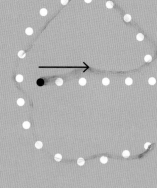

f is for fish

Peppa and George have a pet fish. Draw your own fish here. Choose a name beginning with **f** - Flippy, Fin or Fred - for your fish.

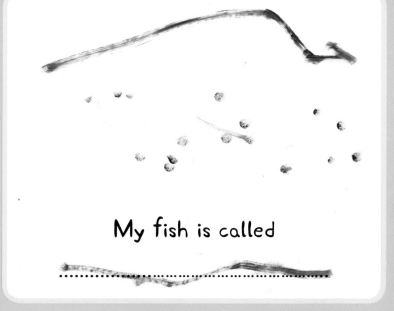

My fish is called

....

g is for guitar

Madame Gazelle loves to play the guitar for the children in her playgroup. Find the sticker of the guitar and stick it here.

h is for house

This is Peppa's house. Draw a picture of your house, and trace over the letters of the word 'house' with your pencil.

a b c d e f g h i j k l m n o p q r s t u v w x y z

i is for insect

Help Peppa and George find the spiders and the butterflies in the garden. Draw a ring around each insect as you spot it.

j is for jack-in-the-box

Boing! Boing! Which jack-in-the-box is the odd one out?

a.

b.

c.

d.

Answer: b.

k is for kite

George loves to fly his kite, high in the sky.
Write a letter **k** on the kite and colour the kite in.

l is for letter

Peppa likes getting letters. Finish this letter to Peppa, telling her about something beginning with l that you have seen today.

Dear Peppa,

Today I saw a

l................................

Love from

....

a b c d e f g h i j k l m n o p q r s t u v w x y z

m is for mud

Splish! Splash! Splosh! Everyone loves to jump in muddy puddles! Colour the picture, and find some mud splat stickers to make the picture really muddy!

n is for newspaper

Daddy Pig likes to relax with the newspaper. Ssshh! Don't make lots of noise. Trace over the letter n with your pencil.

o is for orange

Peppa likes eating oranges. Look at all this fruit! Draw a ring around all the oranges you can see.

p is for pig, Peppa Pig

Draw something here for Peppa beginning with the letter P.

I have drawn a p..........................

a b c d e f g h i j k l m n o p q r s t u v w x y z

q is for queen

A queen wears a crown like Peppa, when Peppa plays dressing up. Draw a crown here. Can you write the letter q on it?

r is for rabbit

Rebecca Rabbit goes to playgroup with Peppa. Colour the books red for Rebecca to read, and trace over the letters of the word **red** with a red pencil.

S is for sheep

Suzy Sheep and Peppa are playing outside. The sun is shining. Find the correct stickers to match each shadow of the two things beginning with the letter **S**.

t is for teddy

Peppa's favourite toy is Teddy. Draw a picture of your teddy, and write some **t's** here.

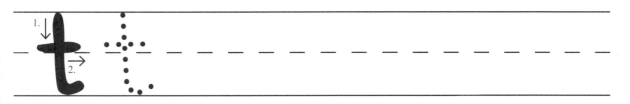

a b c d e f g h i j k l m n o p q r s t u v w x y z

U is for umbrella

Drip! Drop! Look at Peppa playing in the rain with her umbrella. Draw an umbrella here and colour it in with your favourite colours.

V is for vegetables

Look at all these yummy vegetables. Which one is different?

a.   b.   c.   d.   e.   f.

Answer: b.

W is for weather

Colour in the sun and the rain cloud.

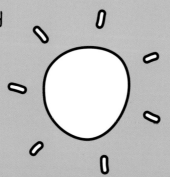

X is for xylophone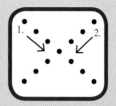

George enjoys playing the xylophone.
Write a letter **X** here.

y is for yellow

Draw a ring around all the yellow things in the picture above.

z is for zebra

Zoe Zebra is having a sleepover with her friends. Find the
sticker of Zoe and then write some more sleepy **z's**.

z z z z

place your
sticker here

a
b
c
d
e
f
g
h
i
j
k
l
m
n
o
p
q
r
s
t
u
v
w
x
y
z

Now you know your ABC, say all the letter sounds with Peppa and her friends. Find the correct stickers and fill in the missing letters.

a   place your sticker here   c   place your sticker here   e   place your sticker here   g   place your sticker here

i   place your sticker here

k

place your sticker here   m

place your sticker here   o

place your sticker here

q

place your sticker here

s   place your sticker here   u   place your sticker here   w   place your sticker here   y   place your sticker here